color me AFFiRMED

AFFIRMATION COLORING BOOK
FOR ADULTS & TEENS

FOR A LITTLE INSPIRATION
follow along at:

◎ @JUNEANDLUCY

👍 @JUNEANDLUCY

WWW. JUNELUCY.COM

✉ **Love free goodies?** Join our newsletter by emailing us at **freebies@junelucy.com** to receive freebies, discounts and sales info. Let us know which book you bought by putting the book title in the subject line of your email.

Shop our other books at
www.junelucy.com

For questions and customer service, email us at
support@junelucy.com

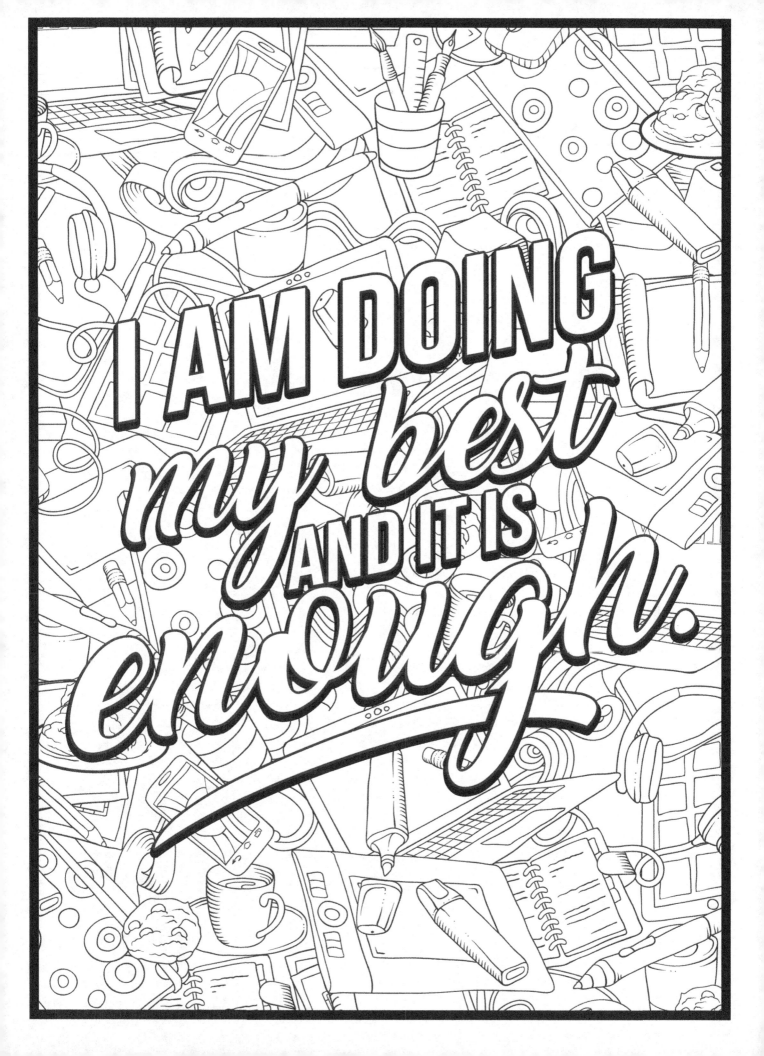

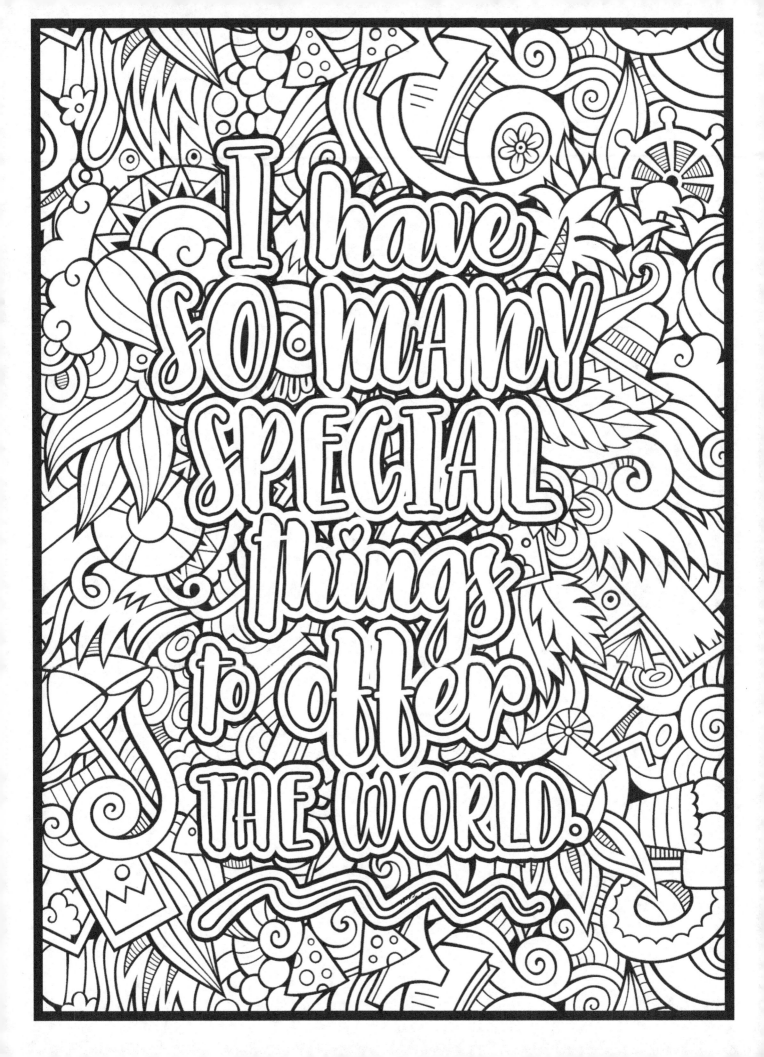

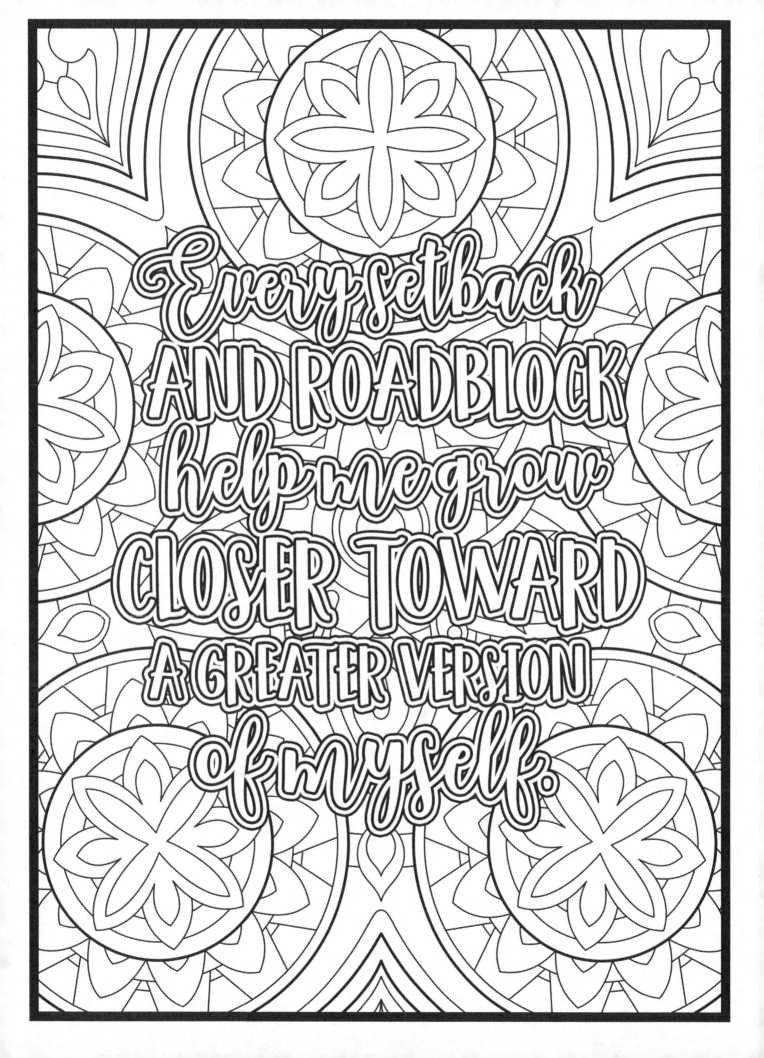

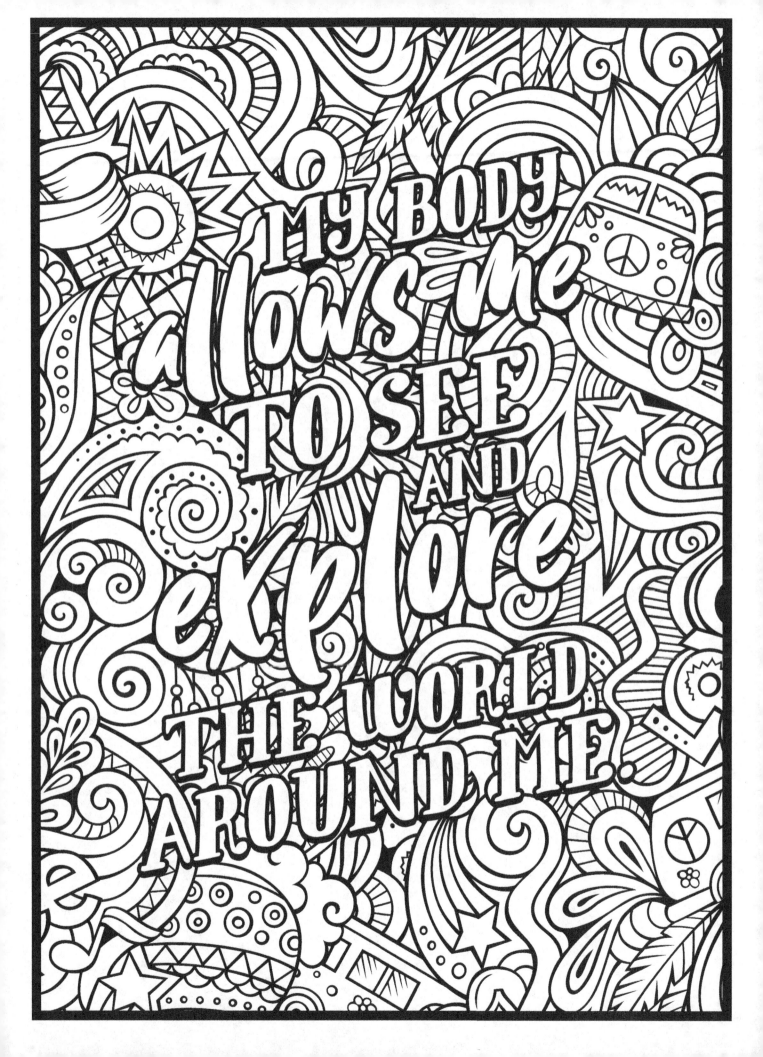

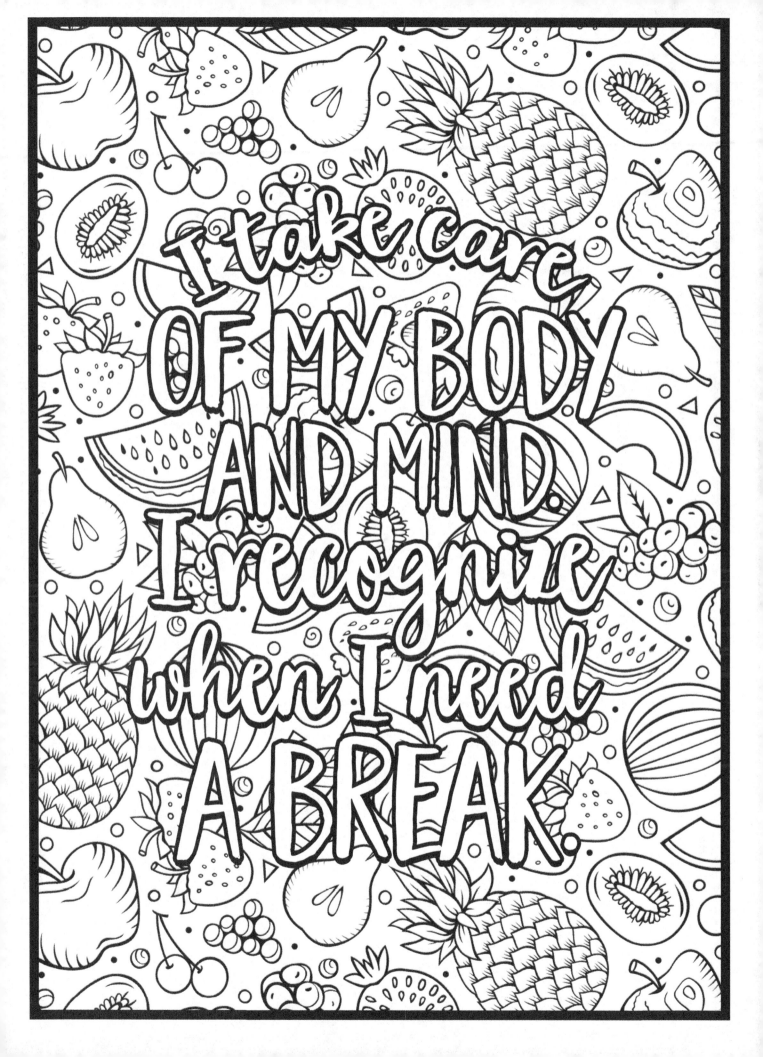

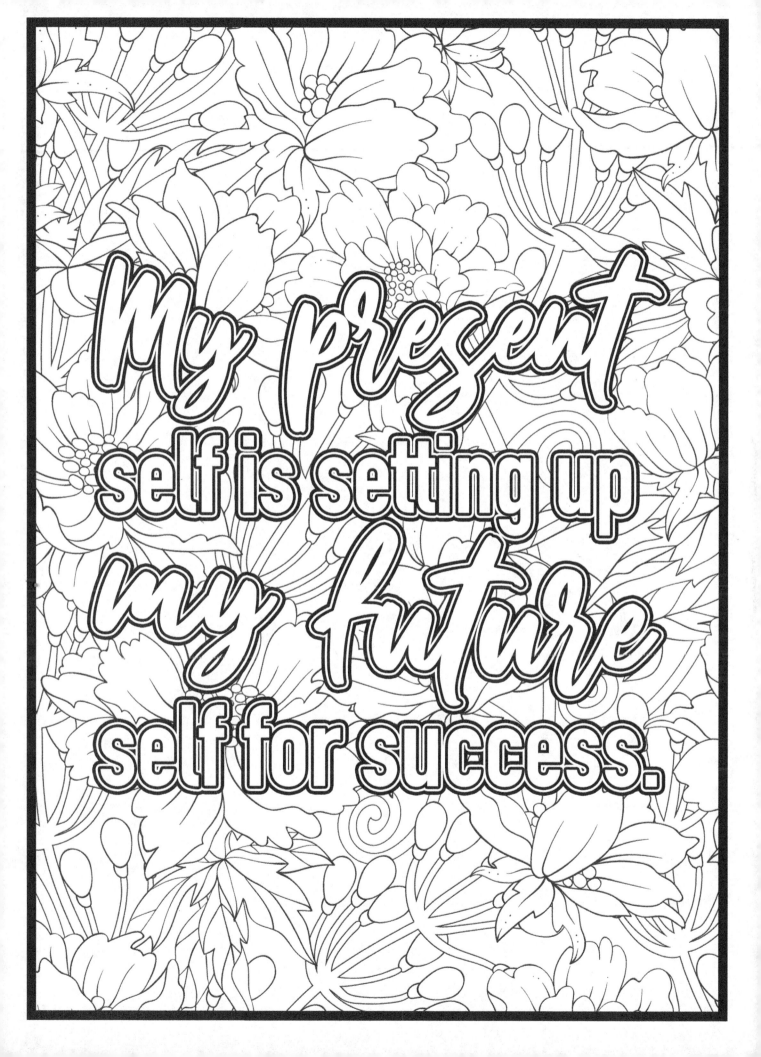

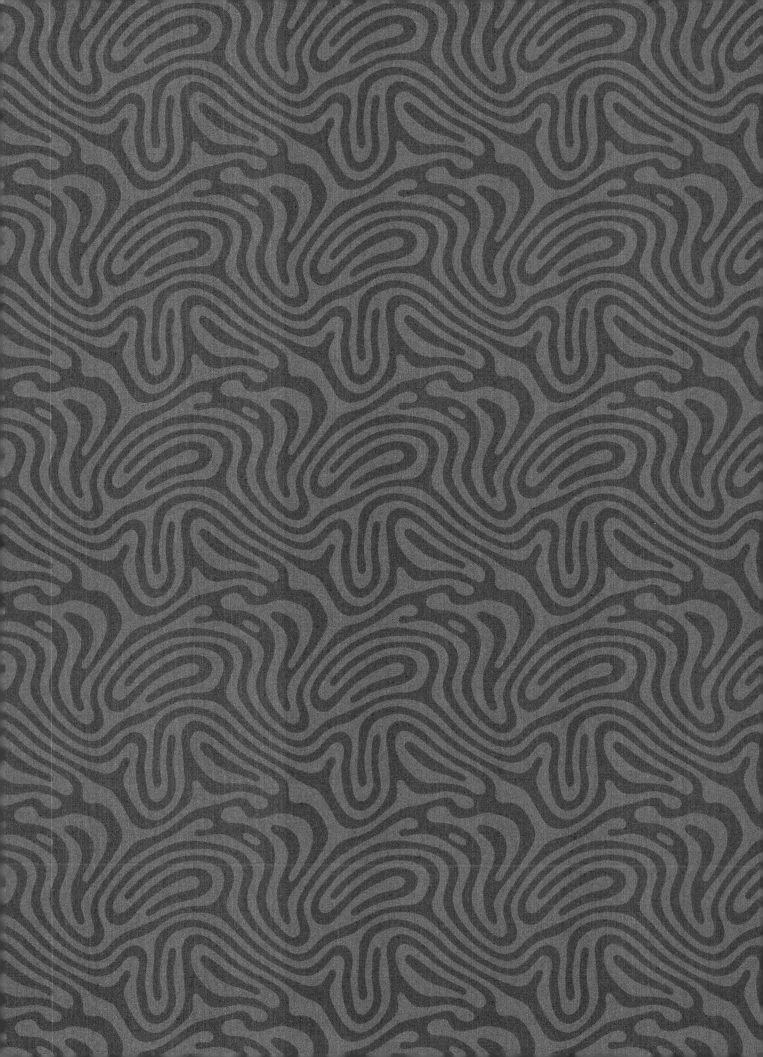

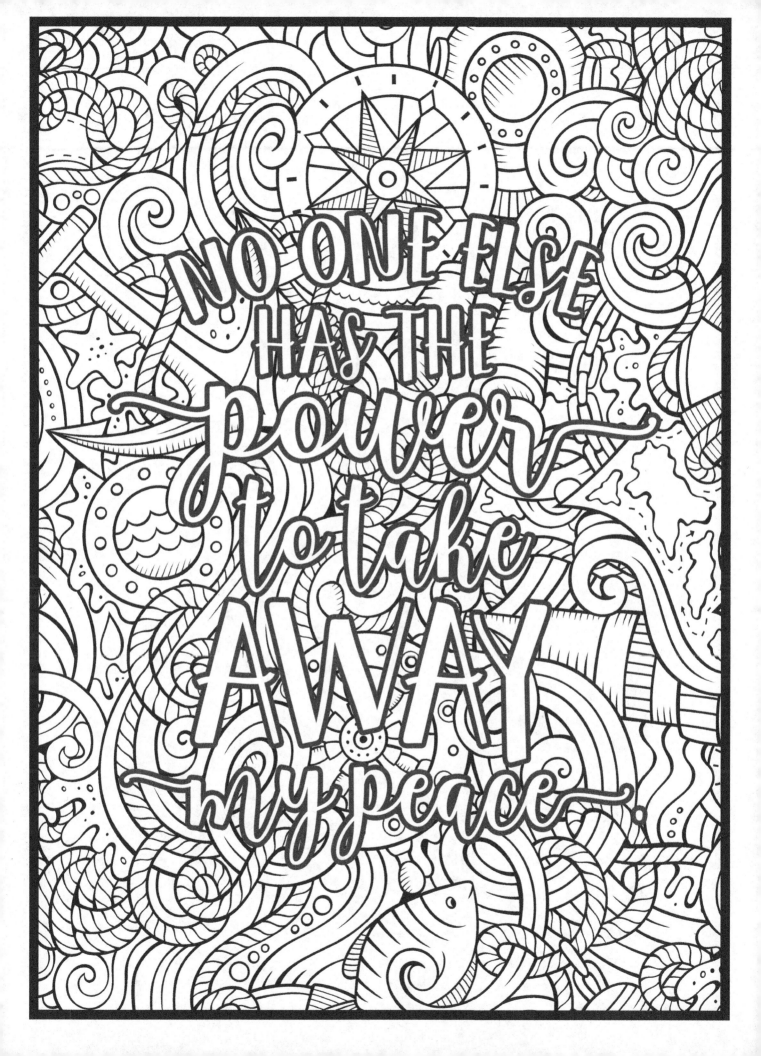

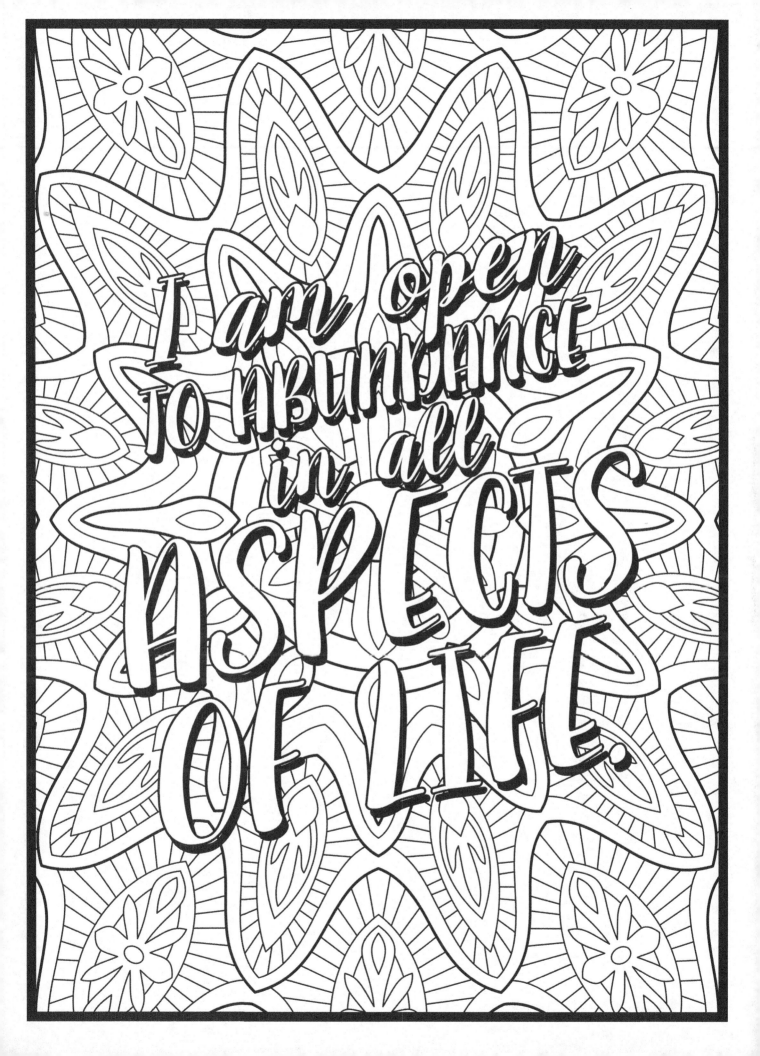

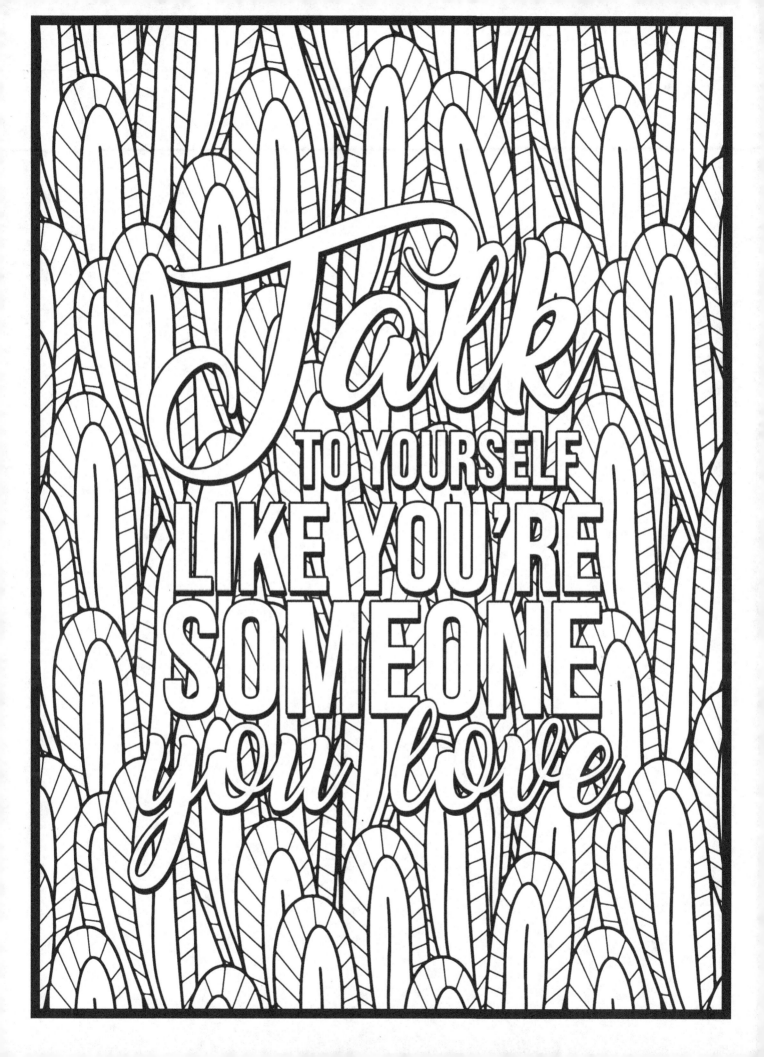